# Theseus and th

## by David C

## Author's note

Stories about a hero who defeats a monster are international and timeless. Theseus and the Minotaur is one of the most famous of these. The fact that the Minotaur is half-human, half-animal makes this story particularly menacing.

The idea of combining different species to create a 'new' creature has fascinated people over the years, in stories and in real life. In real laboratories, scientists have now created a Liger (half-lion, half-tiger) and a Cama (half-camel, half-llama).

# The Cast

**Periboea**  a young maiden of Athens.

**Hermus**  a young Athenian man.

**Aegeus**  King of Athens.

**Theseus**  Son of Aegeus.

Minos **King of Crete.**

Ariadne **Daughter of Minos.**

Asterion, the Minotaur **– half-man, half-bull.**

Nausitheus **a helmsman.**

The guard at the palace of King Minos.

Young men and women from Athens.

Guards.

# Act 1: **In Athens**

**Periboea (as narrator)**

How well I remember that terrible day in April when the King called all the young men and women to the temple!

**Hermus (as narrator)**

How could we forget it? We were all terrified that we would be chosen ...

**Aegeus** Young people of Athens! The day has come when we must choose fourteen of you – seven men and seven maidens – to be sent to King Minos of Crete, and be sacrificed to the Minotaur. Every seven years we must make this sacrifice.

If you are chosen, be brave, for it is the will of the gods!

**Periboea (as narrator)**

All our names were written on tablets. The tablets of the men were in one cauldron, the maidens in another. Slowly, the King pulled out the tablets and read out the names ...

*(Aegeus draws the next tablet from one of the cauldrons.)*

**Aegeus** **Periboea is the next to be chosen!**

**Periboea (as narrator)**

I almost fainted as my name was read out.

8

**Hermus (as narrator)**

Me too! But I tried to be brave, as the King had said.

**Periboea (as narrator)**

Just then the King's son, Theseus, stepped forward. What a fine man he looked!

**Hermus (as narrator)**

Some people say he has two fathers, and that one of them is the god, Poseidon!

**Theseus** **Father, this sacrifice of our young people has gone on long enough!**

You have drawn out the names of six men. Draw no more, for I will go to Crete as a sacrifice! I will either die there, or destroy the Minotaur, and remove this terrible burden on our city forever!

**Aegeus** Theseus, you are brave, but foolish! Please think carefully. Sending these young people to their deaths is hard enough. I could not bear to lose my own son!

**Theseus**  This is something I must do, Father! Each day, wait for me on the cliff tops. If I have been successful, I will hoist white sails. If I have been killed, the ship will fly its black sails.

Come on, you chosen ones! Say goodbye to your families. If the gods are with us, you will see them again!

## Hermus (as narrator)

We all believed in Theseus, but we still felt terrified all the way to Crete! We kept thinking about the Minotaur, and the terrible way that we might die in his Labyrinth!

# Act 2: **Arriving in Crete**

**Periboea (as narrator)**

At last we saw the shores of Crete rising up out of the Mediterranean. Minos, the King of Crete, was waiting for us at the harbour, with his daughter, Ariadne. I didn't like the look of the King at all.

**Hermus (as narrator)**

He certainly was an evil-looking character! We all filed off the ship, with Theseus in the lead.

**Minos**  At last! Hurry up, the Minotaur is hungry for blood! *(To Theseus)* You are first off the ship. You will be the first to die!

**Theseus**  Perhaps not, Minos! I am Theseus, son of Aegeus and of Poseidon! I intend

to kill that monster
of yours!

**Minos**     *(laughing)* **Son of a god,
eh? You'll have to
prove that, young man!**
*(He throws his ring into
the sea.)* **Jump into the
sea and get my ring
back. If you can't,
you'll die on the spot!**

## Hermus (as narrator)

Theseus jumped into the sea. He
was gone a long time and we
were all getting worried!

## Periboea (as narrator)

At last, he climbed out of the water with the ring in his hand! Everyone cheered and clapped. That really annoyed Minos!

## Hermus (as narrator)

We were all led away to our prison to wait our turn to enter the Labyrinth. Theseus was to be the first. We prayed he could save us!

# Act 3: **Inside the Labyrinth**

**Periboea (as narrator)**

That night, Ariadne went to see Theseus ...

**Ariadne** **Theseus, I want to help you kill that dreadful monster. Look what I've brought.**

**Theseus** **A ball of string? What use is that?**

**Ariadne** **It is enchanted string. Tie it to the doorpost of the Labyrinth.**

It will unwind itself,
and lead you to the
Minotaur. When you
have killed it, follow
the string back to
the entrance!

Theseus Why are you helping
me? Your father would
kill you if he knew.

**Ariadne** When I saw you coming off the ship, I fell in love with you. I will help you, but you must promise to take me back to Athens and marry me!

**Periboea (as narrator)**

Theseus agreed. Soon after, the guards came to take him to the Labyrinth.

**Hermus (as narrator)**

Once inside the vast maze, no one had ever found their way out again.

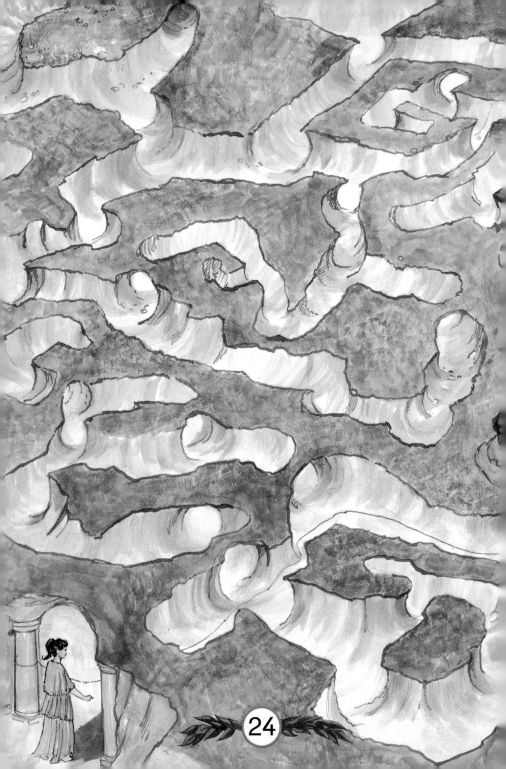

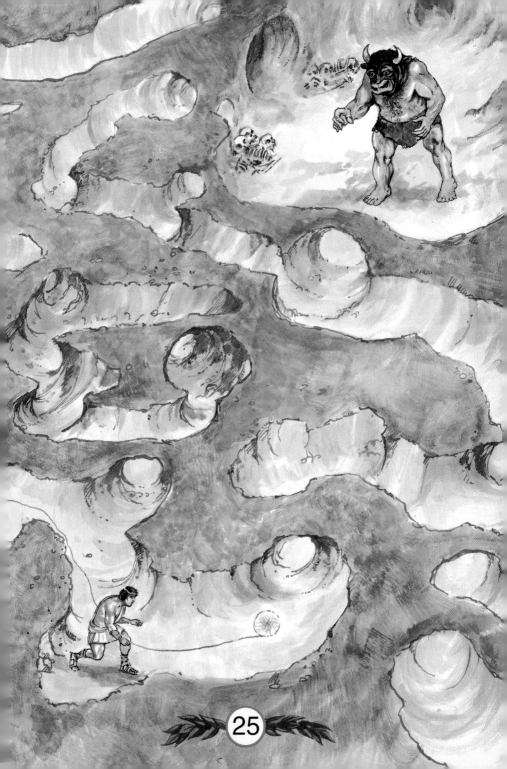

**Theseus** I can see why everyone gets lost in here. There are passages in all directions! There goes the string. I hope Ariadne isn't tricking me. Well, whatever happens, I'll meet the Minotaur sooner or later!

*(Theseus sets off down a passage, following the ball of string. It leads him to the centre of the Labyrinth.)*

**Asterion** *(under his breath)* **Here comes my next victim!** *(To Theseus)* **Get ready to die!**

**Theseus** Not this time, Asterion!

**Asterion** A brave one, eh? I like them best. A good fight gives me an appetite!

*(Theseus and the Minotaur fall to the ground, struggling.)*

**Hermus (as narrator)**
It was a long and bloody battle. Asterion was the deadliest enemy Theseus had ever faced.

**Periboea (as narrator)**
At last the fight was over and the Minotaur lay dead on the floor.

**Theseus** Now to find my way out of here! Then I shall rescue my friends, and sail back to Athens!

**Periboea (as narrator)**

Ariadne was waiting for Theseus at the door of the Labyrinth.

**Ariadne** **Is the Minotaur dead?**

**Theseus** **Yes, he's dead, but it was a very hard battle.**

**Ariadne** **Don't forget your promise to take me to Athens and marry me.**

**Theseus** **I haven't forgotten. Go to the harbour and see**

Nausitheus, the helmsman of our ship. Give him this token so that he knows the message comes from me. Tell him to prepare the boat and be ready to leave at a moment's notice!

## Periboea (as narrator)

Theseus crept up to our prison and killed the guards outside. More guards arrived, but the young men were released by now and they soon dealt with them. We women joined in too! We all set off for the harbour. Minos's soldiers were behind us, but we got safely to the ship.

## Hermus (as narrator)

Nausitheus was ready for us and we were soon at sea. By the time the Cretans managed to launch a ship, we were gone.

I could just imagine the scene at the King's palace when he heard the news!

**Guard**  **Your majesty! The Athenians have escaped! We tried to stop their ship leaving the harbour, but we were too late!**

**Minos**  **What! You let them escape? You fool! You will be sent to the Minotaur for this!**

**Guard**  I'm afraid the Minotaur is dead – Theseus killed him!

**Minos**  This is the most terrible news, and you will die for bringing it! Before I kill you, fetch me my daughter, Ariadne, so that she can comfort me!

**Guard**  I've got some bad news about Ariadne as well ...

# Act 5: **Back to Athens**

**Hermus (as narrator)**

On the way back to Athens we stopped at the island of Naxos. We needed to take on water and food, as we had left Crete in such a hurry.

**Ariadne**  **I'm glad to be back on dry land. I don't like being at sea at all!**

**Theseus**  **Why don't you go over to those sunny rocks and have a good sleep?**

I'll give you a call when we're ready to go.

**Ariadne** That would be really good. I haven't slept a wink on board.

*(Ariadne falls asleep.)*

**Nausitheus** *(To Theseus)* **All ready, sir. We have enough food and water to reach Athens.**

**Theseus** Thank you, Nausitheus. Hoist the sails, and let's be off!

**Nausitheus** But what about Ariadne? I'd better wake her up!

**Theseus** No, she's very tired. Let her sleep.

**Periboea (as narrator)**

We couldn't believe it when Theseus left Ariadne sleeping on the beach. Perhaps he didn't love her. Or perhaps he thought it would be a bad idea to bring home someone from Crete – Cretans weren't very popular in Athens!

**Hermus (as narrator)**

Yes, we all thought it was a dirty trick. But he had saved our lives and, anyway, none of us was brave enough to argue with Theseus!

**Nausitheus**    **Land ho!**

**Periboea (as narrator)**

Home at last! We were all so relieved to see Athens again. The trouble was that with everything that had happened, Theseus had forgotten something important ...

**Nausitheus** Look, Theseus! There are crowds of people waiting on the cliff tops to greet us! I can hear them cheering!

**Theseus** They're not cheering, they're wailing and groaning! There's my father, look, he's jumping into the sea!

**Hermus (as narrator)**

Then Theseus looked up at the sails, and remembered what he had told his father, Aegeus.

**Theseus** **Each day, wait for me on the cliff tops. If I have been successful, I will hoist white sails. If I have been killed, the ship will fly its black sails ...**

**Periboea (as narrator)**

From the masts of our ship, the black sails were drawing us closer towards Athens ...

**Hermus (as narrator)**

To Athens, where Theseus, despite his sorrow and guilt, would become our new King.